My dear 500 friends

Embalmed and Treasured Up by

GEORGE PRICE

SIMON AND SCHUSTER • NEW YORK • 1963

PUBLISHED BY SIMON AND SCHUSTER, INC.
ROCKEFELLER CENTER, 630 FIFTH AVENUE
NEW YORK 20, N.Y.

FIRST PRINTING

Thirteen of these identified drawings were either revised or redrawn especially for this album.

LIBRARY OF CONGRESS CATALOG CARD NUMBER: 63-19279
MANUFACTURED IN THE UNITED STATES OF AMERICA

"Stop saying 'I wonder what this one can be'!"

"But after Ed Sullivan, then what?"

"Mr. Clean gets rid of dirt and grime and grease
In just a minute.
Mr. Clean will clean your whole house
And everything that's in it."

1

2

RK'S UMPIRE SCHOOL

"All right, it's starting to come down a little heavier. Now would you call the game?"

3

4

5

6

7

"I can't tonight, Ed."

"We're not watching any show. I'm afraid we've watched one too many already."

SHOES
89¢

"It's a typographical error, but have no mercy on me."

WATCH
THIS
WINDOW

"Will you gift-wrap it, please, and join me in a chorus of 'Happy Birthday to You'?"

"If you shouldn't make it, old girl, I'll tell them back home that you gave it your best."

"A powerful glass, sir. Looks like I'm right on top of you, doesn't it?"

Ocean Grove

"Will you please listen to me for a minute?"

"This is the janitor, Mr. McKeester.
We're going to have to shut off the water for a few hours."

"Ah, another precinct heard from!"

" 'Pack up your troubles in your old kit bag and smile, smile, smile.' "

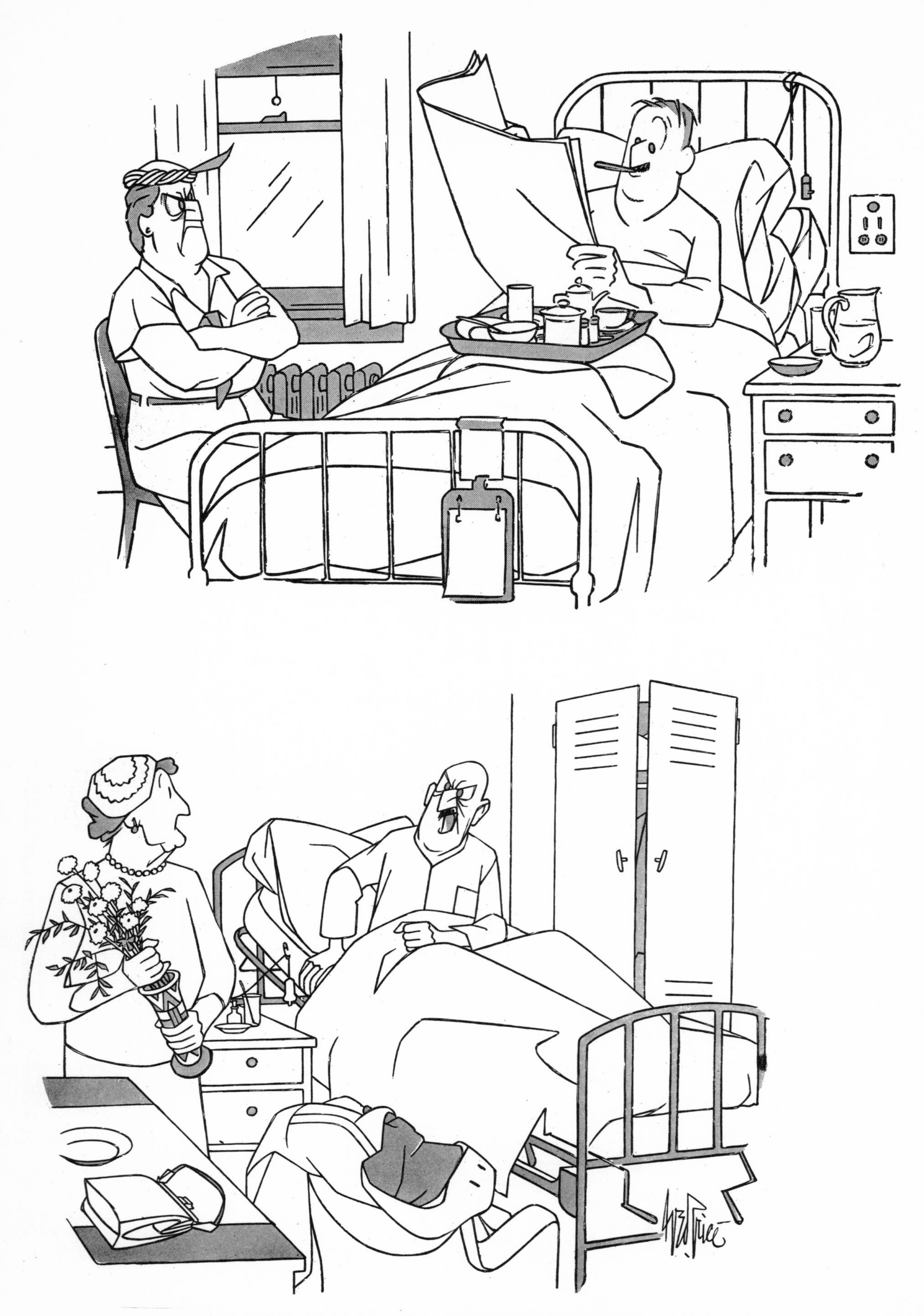

"Mildred, leave those alone! You have no jurisdiction in this room."

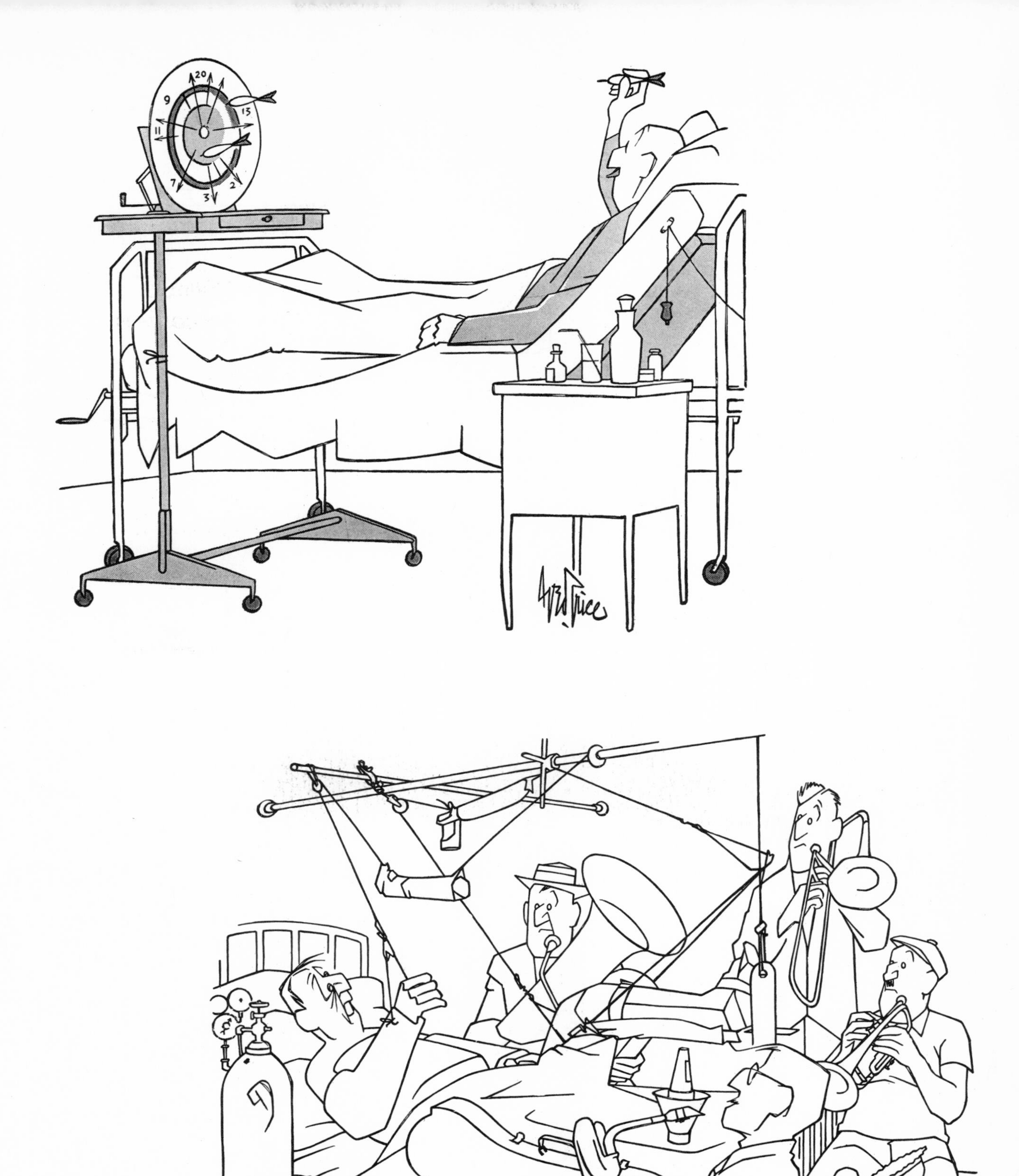
20
9
15
11
7
2
3

"I appreciate your thoughtfulness, boys. It's just that I'm not in the mood for music."

"When you drive, I lock up. When I drive, you lock up. Right?"

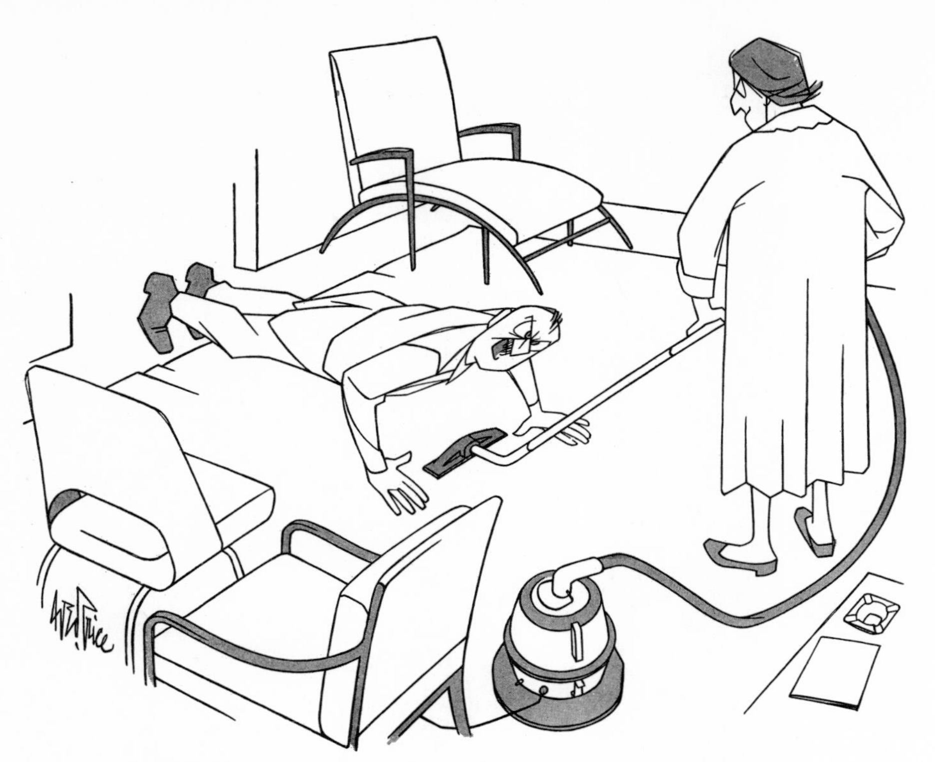

"Can't you wait until I've finished my pushups?"

85¢ TO 6 PM
$1 50

"This way, if we get caught we'll have public sentiment with us."

"All right, Garvey, you've had your chance. Now we're coming in."

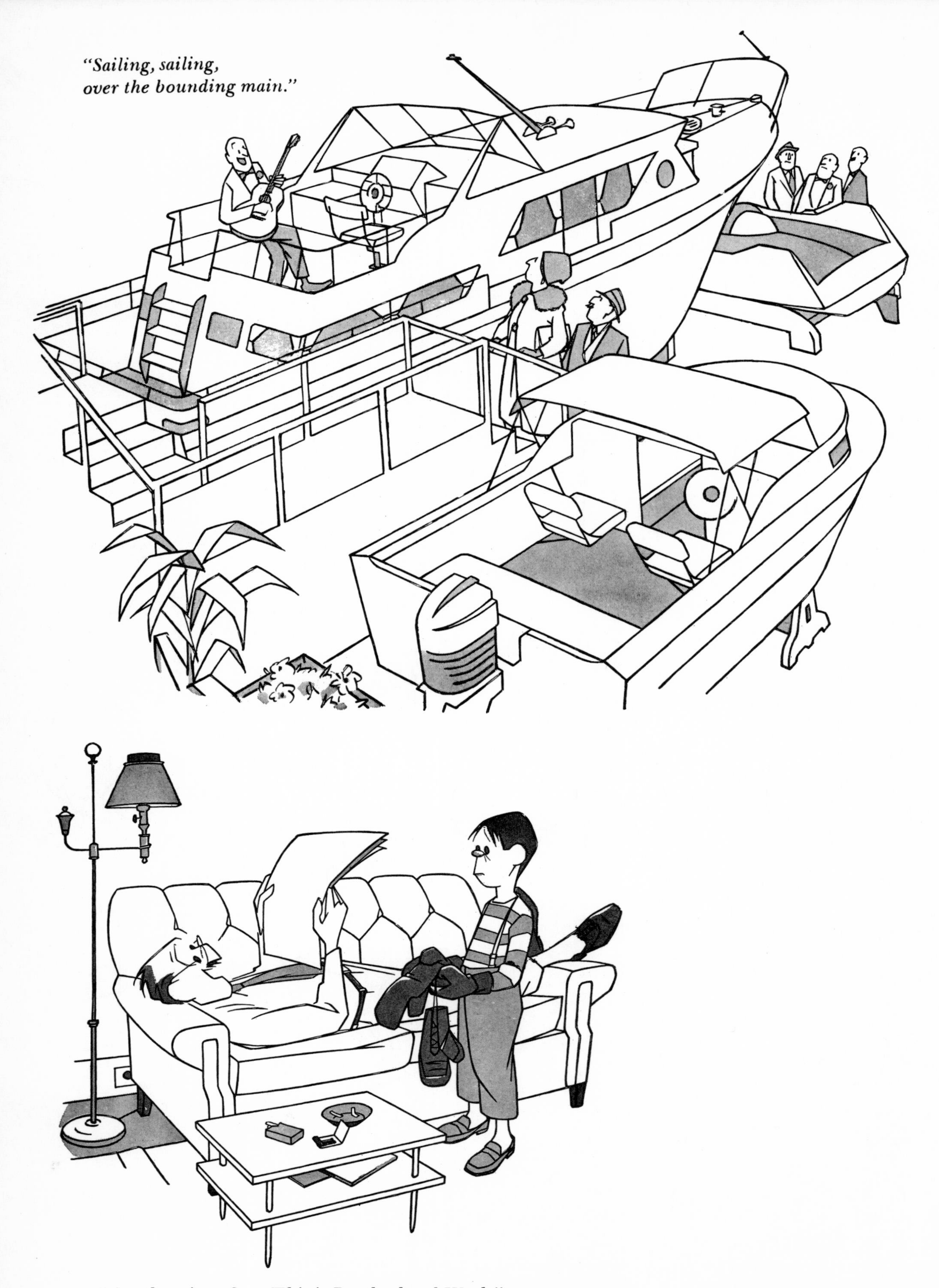

"Sailing, sailing,
over the bounding main."

"Another time, Son. This is Brotherhood Week."

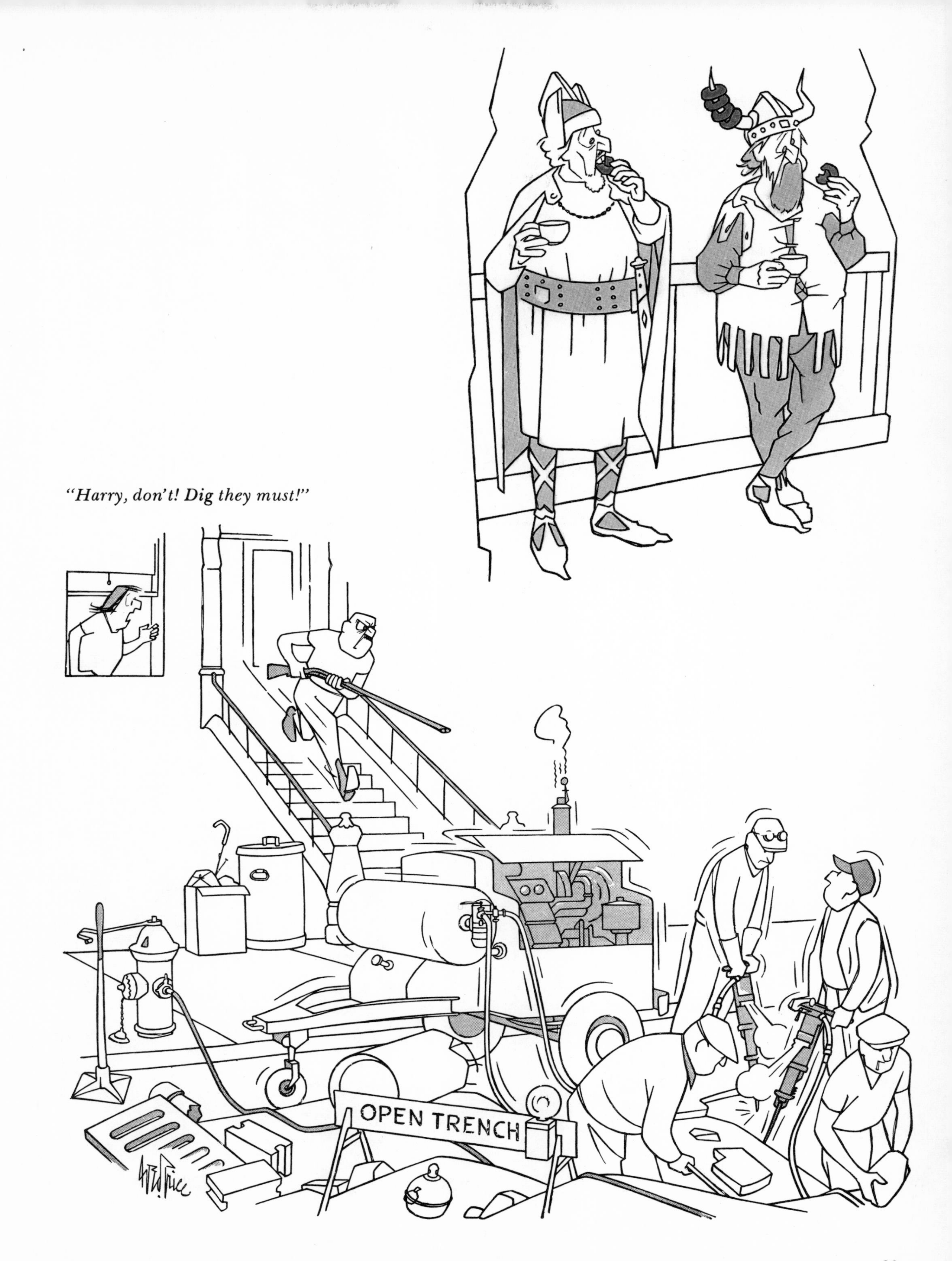
OPEN TRENCH

"Harry, don't! Dig they must!"

"Hey, Mom! Pop's home!"

301
303

"May I? I want to give him the will to live."

BAR

"I think you'll like the spirit of hostility that prevails here."

"You know how it is. You have a little more, you live a little better."

"And just for kicks you could add a third."

"Van Cliburn he's not."

"I really think the tweed suits your rough-and-tumble style, sir."

ADJUSTMENTS

"No, Madam, I will not step outside and settle it!"

"To Augie it's more than just a job."

"Good news, Mr. Murdock! You can go home as soon as you fork over $593.50."

CHENILLE
EMBLEMS
For Club and Team
ACE
Tattoo Transfers
Comic
Buttons
m Stickers
Novelty
Badges

"I'd like to look at it in the dawn's early light."

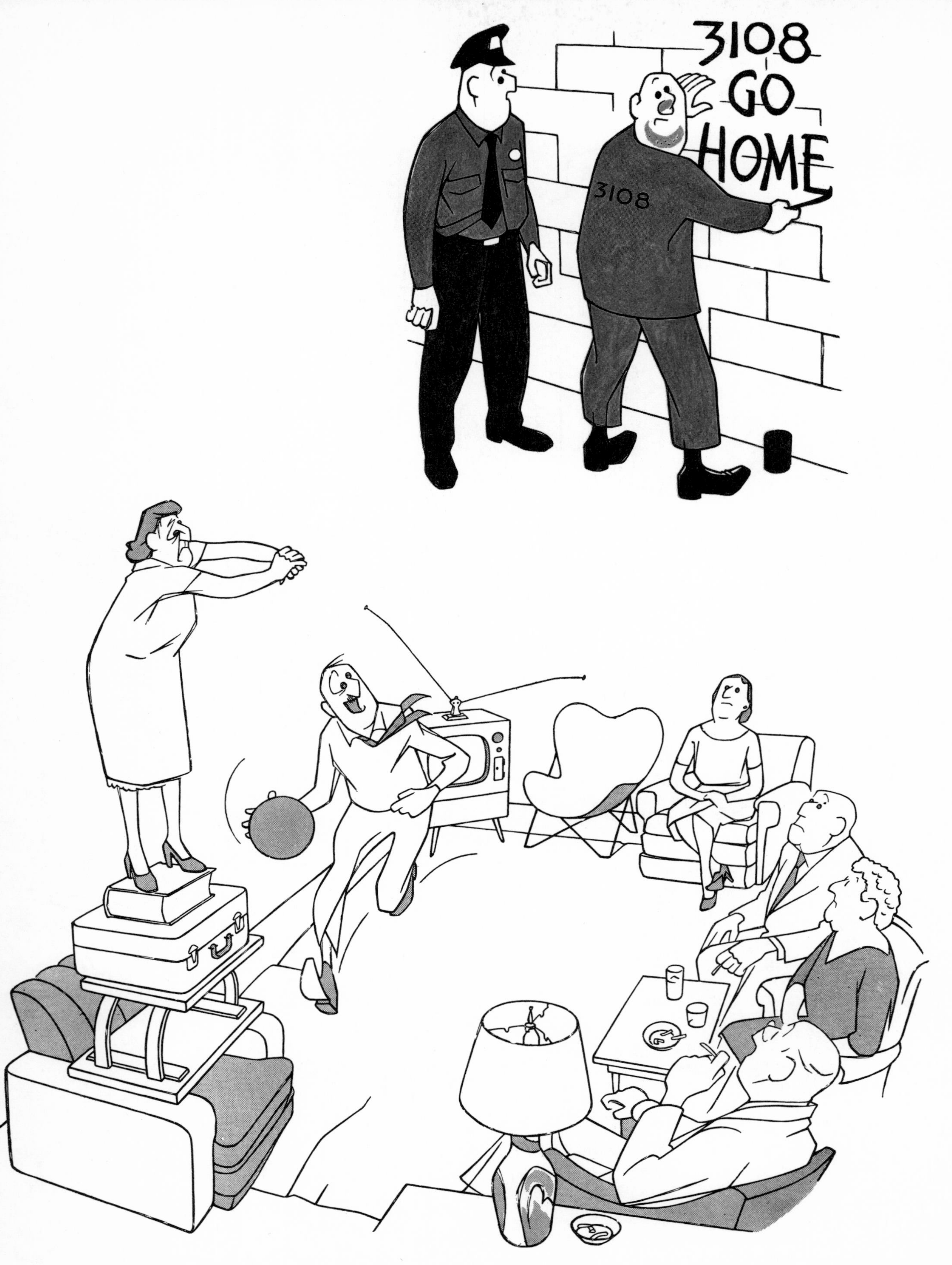
3108 GO HOME
3108

"Then in 1927, against Clinton High, with only two minutes to play..."

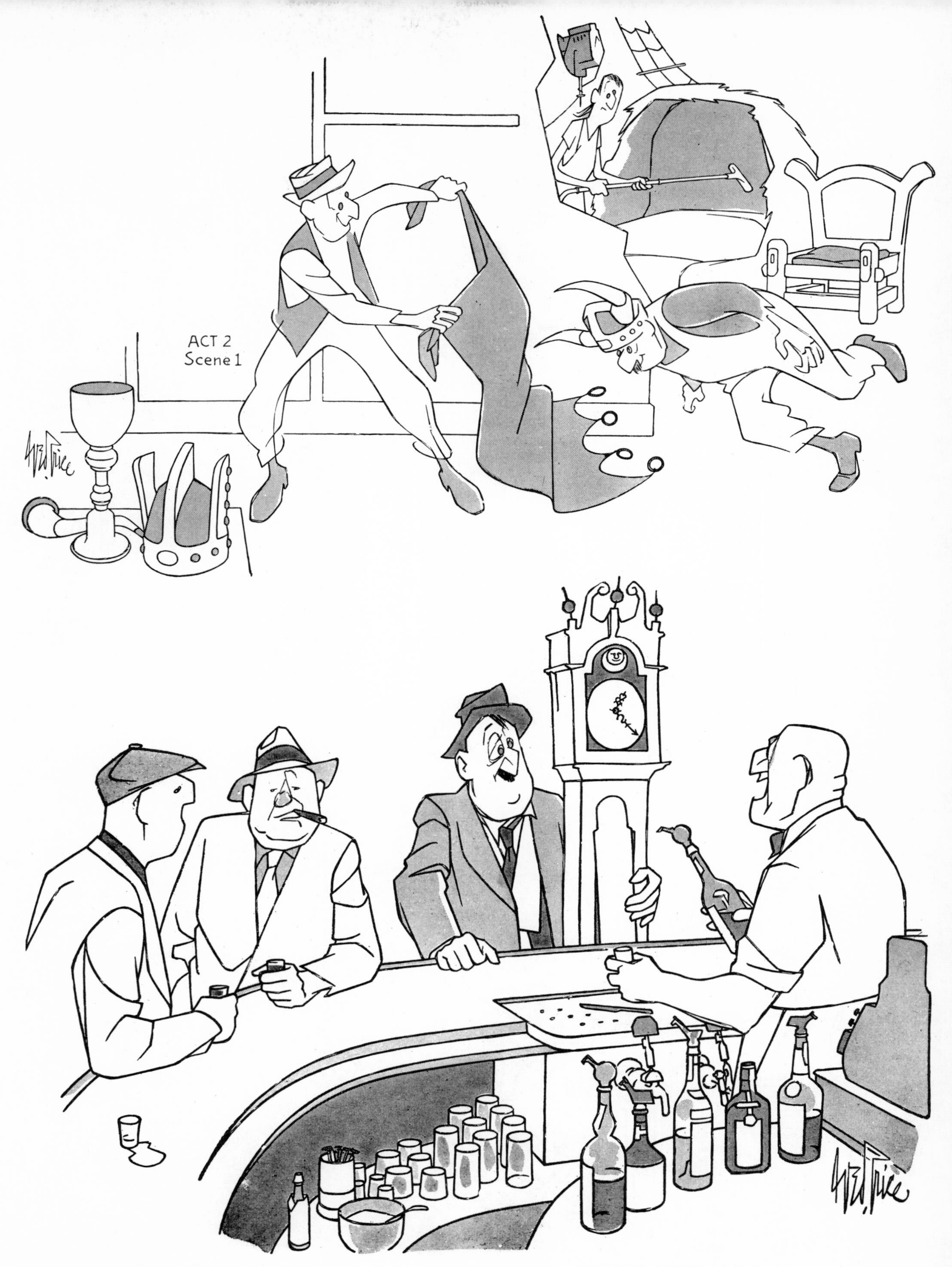
ACT 2
Scene 1

"O.K., but just one bong and out you both go."

"You have to admire his perseverance."

"What better way to say Merry Christmas?"

"Whew! 'Tain't a fit night out for man nor beast!"

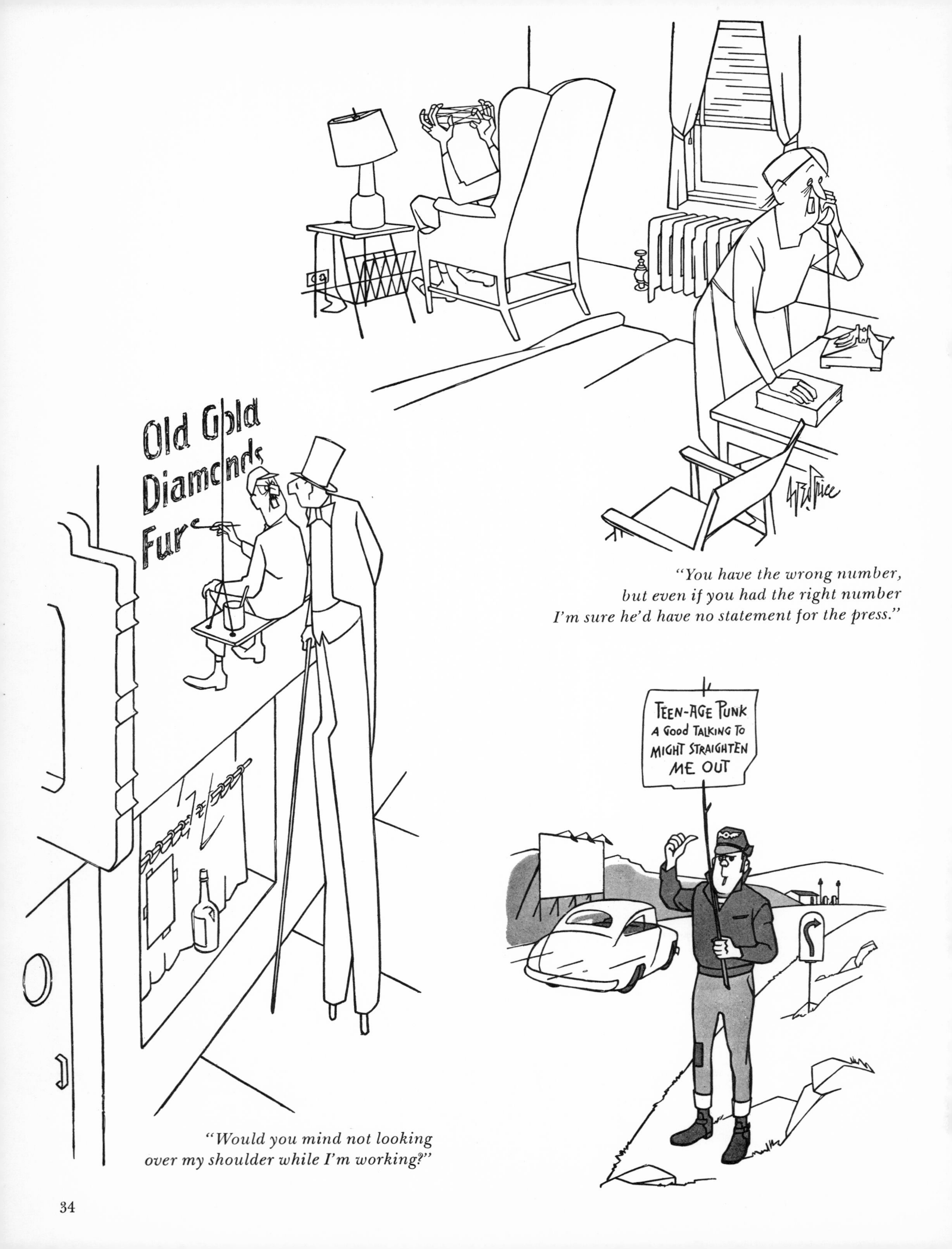
Old Gold
Diamonds
Furs
TEEN-AGE PUNK
A GOOD TALKING TO
MIGHT STRAIGHTEN
ME OUT

"You have the wrong number, but even if you had the right number I'm sure he'd have no statement for the press."

"Would you mind not looking over my shoulder while I'm working?"

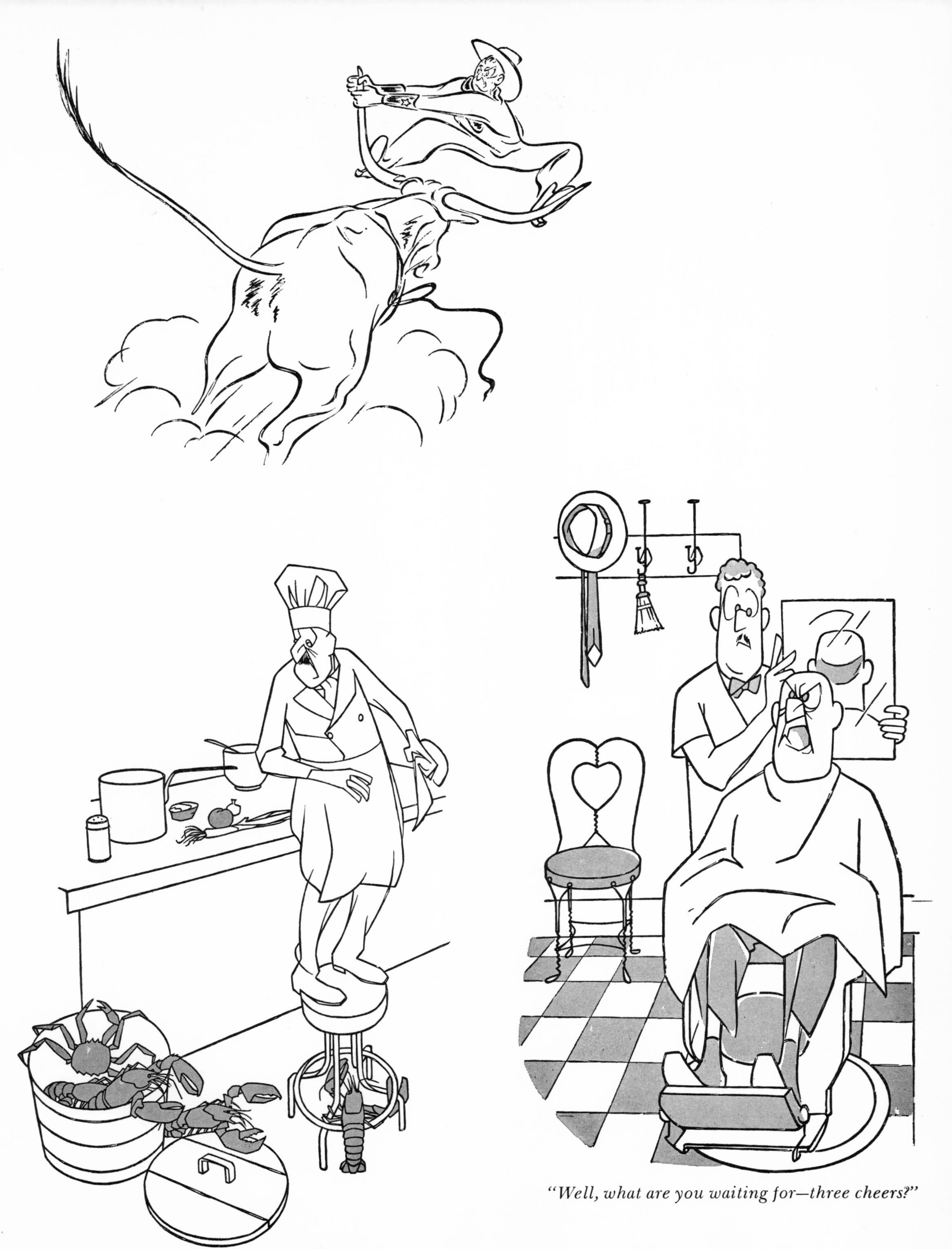

"Well, what are you waiting for—three cheers?"

Dodgers

"Sometimes I wonder if I did right giving him that combination thermometer, hygrometer, barometer, and wind-speed gauge."

"Don't you 'Comrade' me!"

INSTANT
FOODS

"It's every man for himself around here when the old sun drops over the yardarm."

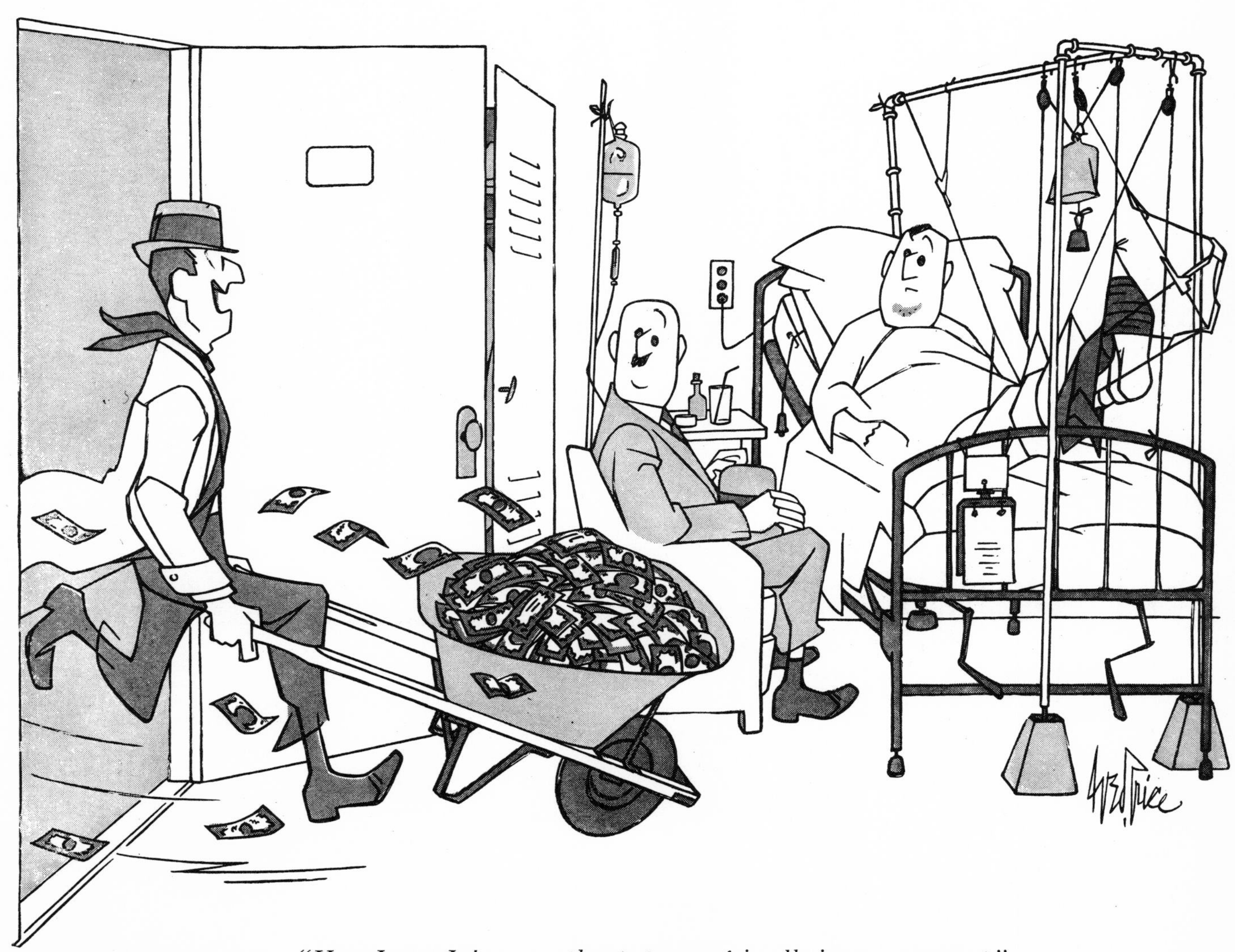

"Here I am—Johnny on the spot, your friendly insurance agent."

"Oven-ready costs a few cents more and oven-ready is worth a few cents more!"

HOT
Peanuts

"It happens I do mind if you just stand there and drink in the aroma."

"We don't get many of his kind around here. He just likes the way the stuff tastes."

"I think you have something to say, all right, but I don't think you're saying it."

72041

"You misunderstood me. I said he could lick any man in the house."

1964

"Here's your twenty bucks. Now scram!"

"Just Molly and me, and baby makes three..."

"Please say when—I'm the type who overdoes things."

DAVE
HARDWARE—HARRY—HOUSEWARE
PRICES Slashed!
HARRY WILL NOT BE UNDER SOLD
AL'S
DAVE

"Come in. You're not interrupting anything."

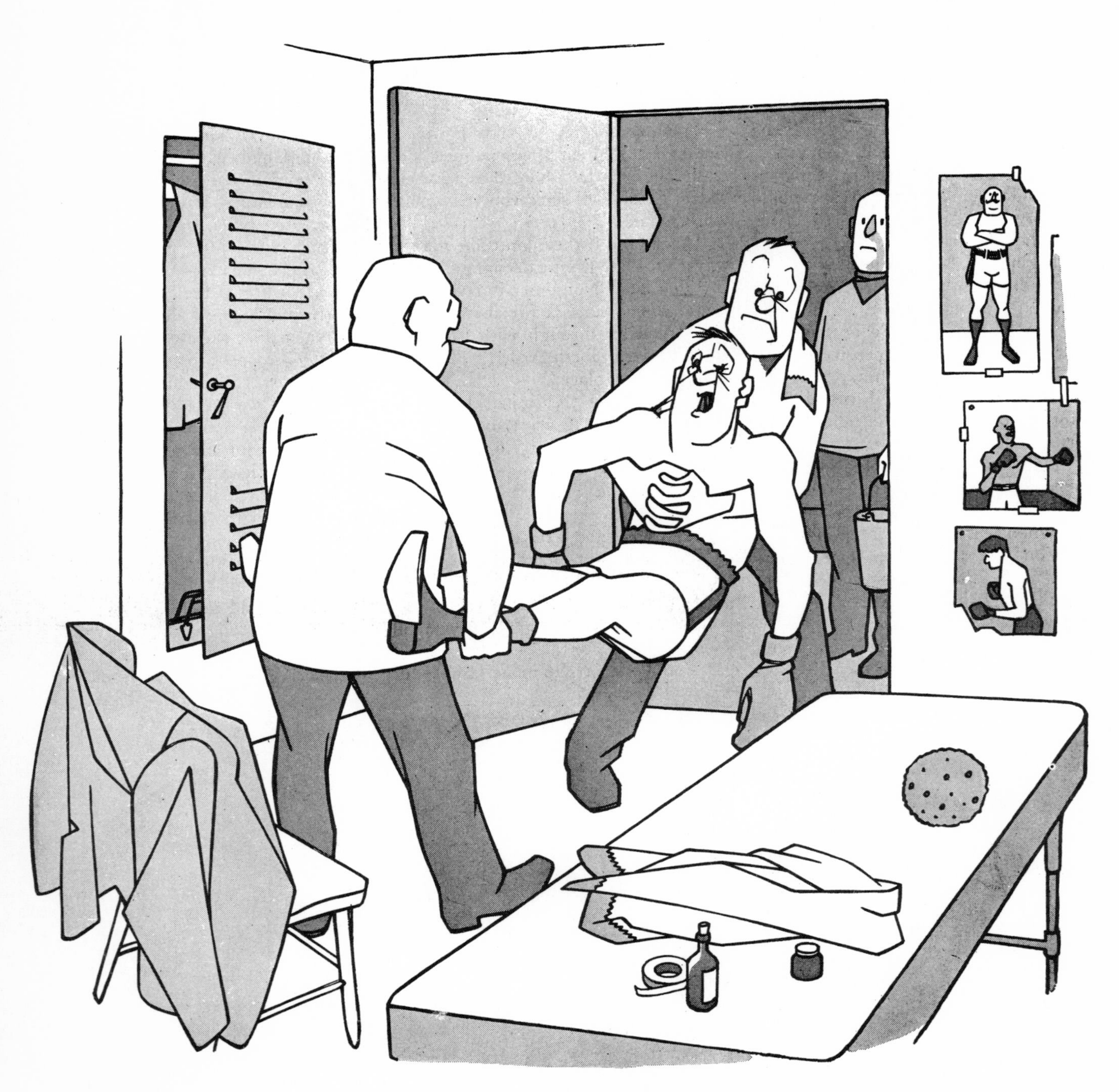

"Tell me this, Ed. Did the fans get their money's worth?"

Catering to the Man on his way Up

"Quite the opposite, I'm afraid. I am a man on his way down."

"Oh, stop griping! We're fulfilling a lifelong dream, aren't we?"

COFFEE 25¢
VARIETY

KEEP
FIT
AT
SAM'S
GYM
LOVER'S
LEAP
Look
before
you
LEAP
25¢

"I'm afraid this can't be much fun for you, dear."

YOUR ONE
DONATION
will take care of
8 BUMS

"You should be on 'What's My Line?'"

"As you can see, it sleeps two very nicely."

"George, what's happened to us?"

"Harry wasn't born great and he hasn't achieved greatness, but he figures there is always the chance that greatness may be thrust upon him."

"We'd like something in a nice roast. We're nine."

"For God's sake, no! Not with my T-square!"

EXIT
ENTRANCE

"Steer clear of 'Under Three Dollars'!"

"Nathaniel's expecting his Civil War Book Club selection today."

"Don't ask me. He leads his life and I lead mine."

"Two blocks straight ahead to Chestnut Street, then right two blocks to Lincoln—you can't miss it; there's a big stone church there—then left, and it's the second house from the corner."

"If you don't want to sing along with Mitch, what do you want to do?"

"You had no trouble scintillating at the Martins'. Why can't you scintillate here?"

"We go to Niagara Falls—he shrugs.
We go to Pike's Peak—he shrugs. We go to the giant redwoods—he shrugs..."

"I'm the captain of this ship!"

"Well, you 'naturally assumed' wrong, suh. Ah happen to want an Alexander."

195
Name your PRICE
No Deal Too Ridiculous
TRY US Don't be embarrassed
Fantastic TRADE IN ALLOWANCE

"The collapsible swimming pool collapsed!"

CHECK HERE

"Was Mommy gone long?"

"Very well, cook him."

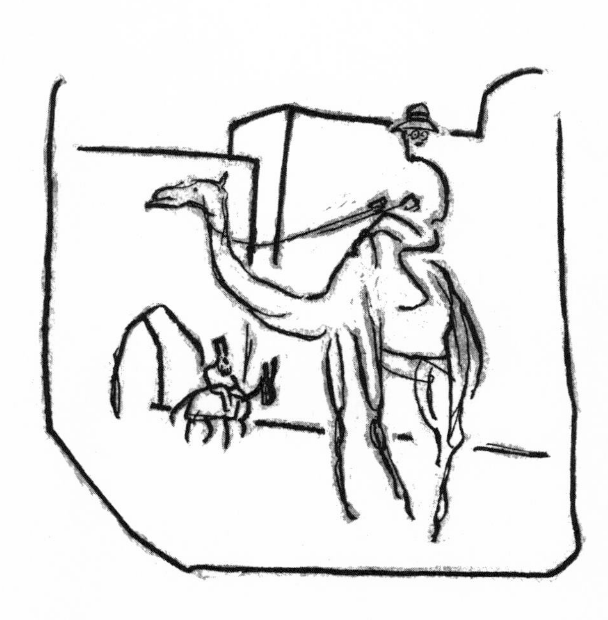

MUSEE
Rue St. Julien le Pauvre . PARIS

"Welcome, stranger! At last I'll have someone to say 'Gesundheit' when I sneeze."

Salzburg

"Watch Brinkley carefully. He tried the soft sell. It didn't work. Now he's trying the hard sell."

"He's the one I was telling you about."

"Well, what's it to be? Yes or no?"

"Scram! You detract from me."

"Do you know of any personal reason why she might want to leave home?"

BUILDING
COMING
DOWN
Must Vacate
Going Out of Business
Entire Stock
SACRIFICED
Bargains
Galore!
BELOW COST

"It's from that matrimonial bureau that introduced us. They want a testimonial."

"Three months we've been here, and still no Welcome Wagon."

GOD BLESS AMERICA
It's Great to be an AMERICAN
FUN BOY
JOKES
NOVELTIES
RIDDLES
DIALECT
MAGIC
TRICKS
Itching Powder
Popeye KNOCKOUT BANK

"I tremble every time he gets another one of those crazy catalogues."

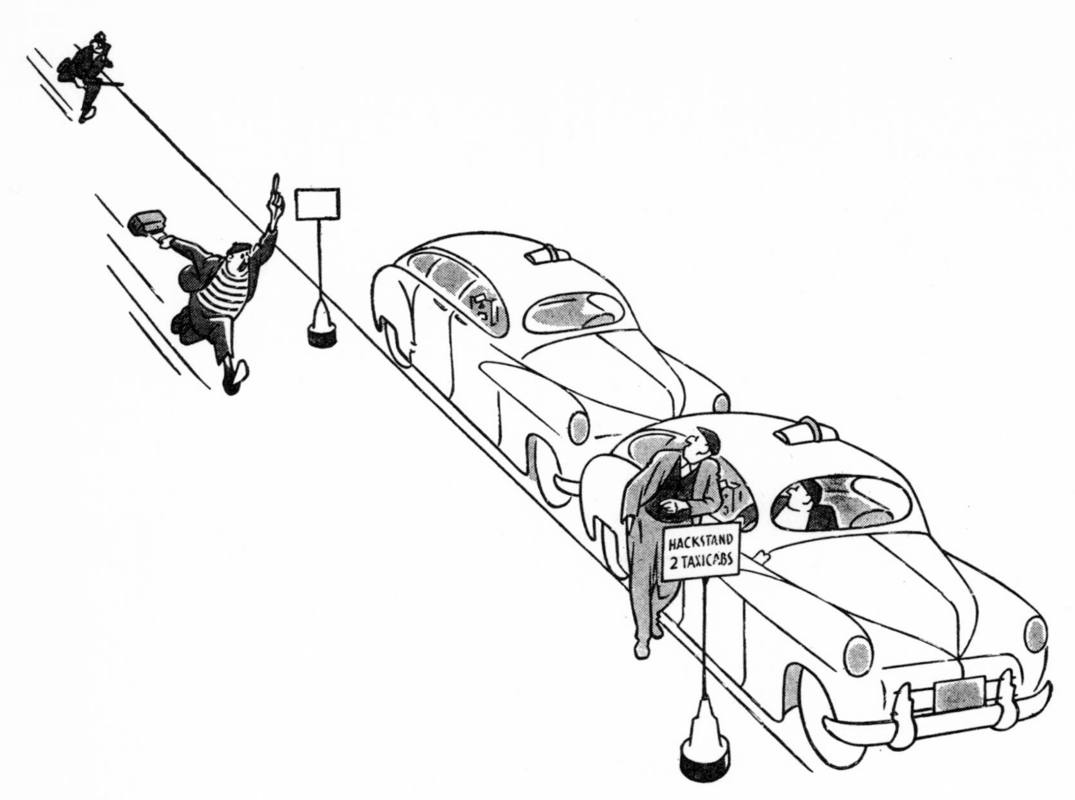
HACKSTAND
2 TAXICABS

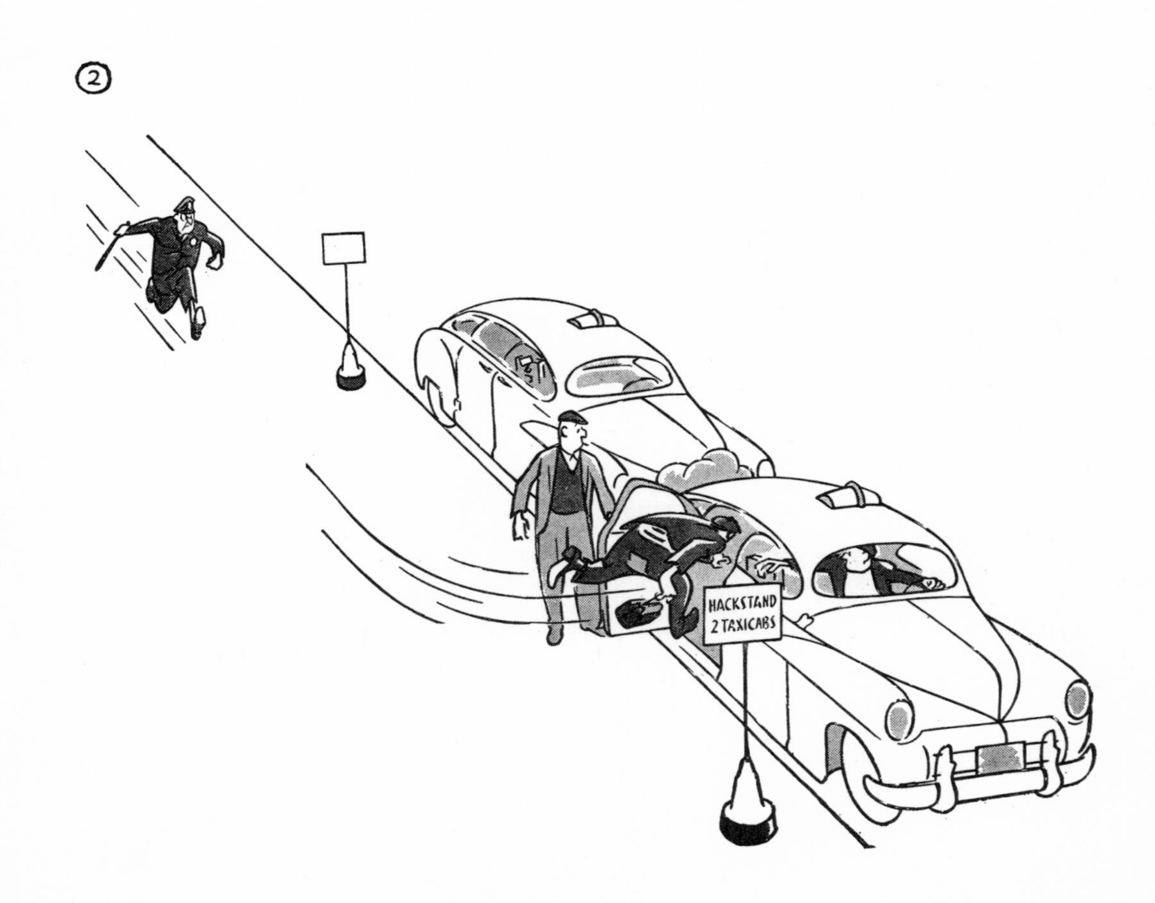
HACKSTAND
2 TAXICABS

HACKSTAND
2 TAXICABS

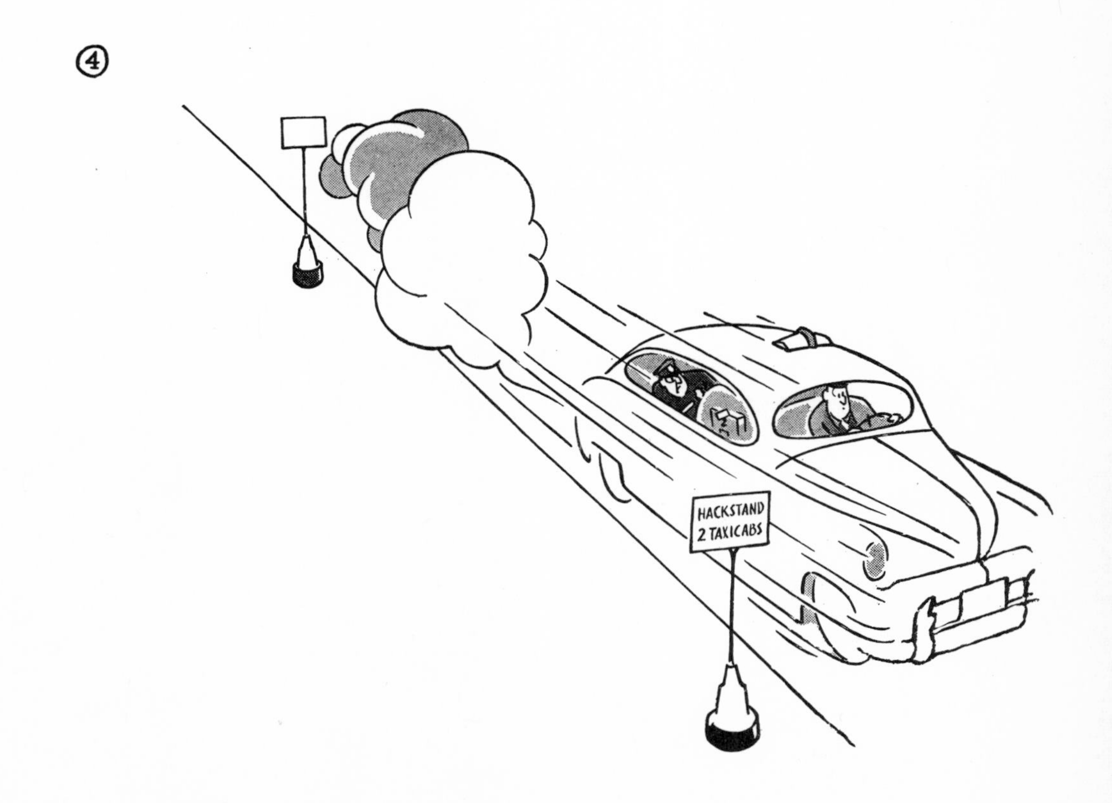
④
HACKSTAND
2 TAXICABS

BAR

"We were a party of four, if you don't mind!"

FIRE

bones 25¢ each

"Here you are, men. Throw them off the scent."

Sale of
TWO-SUITERS

" "There, does that convince you?"

"I like the way you wrinkle your nose when you laugh."

"Vending without a license—and get over here quick!"

"Back to Westport, you crumb!"

"Where did we go wrong?"

" 'Vogue'! And hurry!"

"A copy of Robert's 'Rules of Order.' "

LATEST WORKOUTS
PAST
The MORNING TELEGRAPH
AQUEDUCT

"Look, dear, I only go to the races in the hope of bringing home a little something extra for you and the children."

Etoile de Hollande
Golden Charm
Viktoria
Roslyn
Peace

"I HEARD that remark!"

"Watch your language, man! That's a Mary Margaret McBride."

INTERNAL
REVENUE
SERVICE
1040
1955

"What he needs is a change of scene.
Why don't you move him to some other window?"

"Well, how do you like it?"

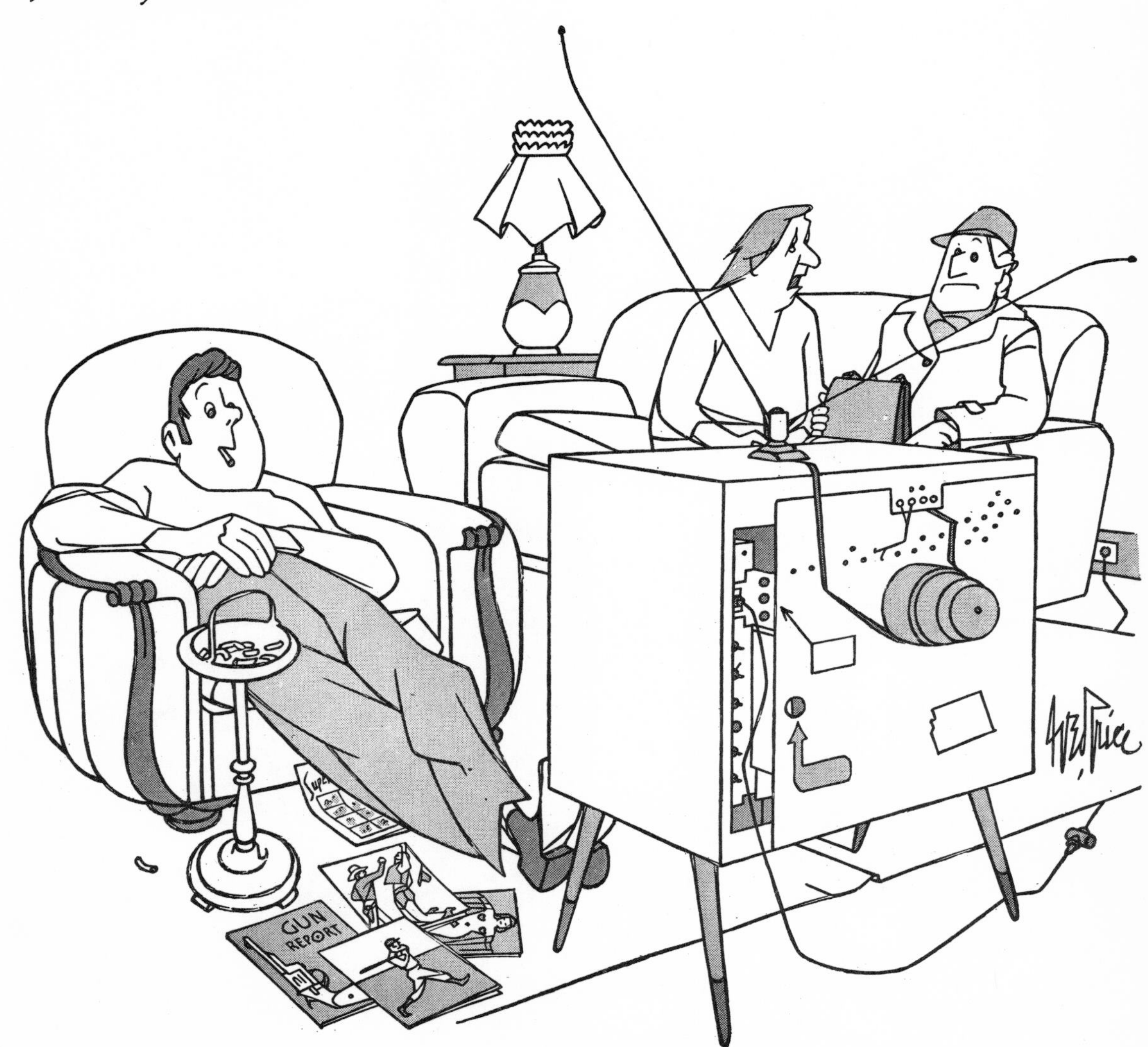
GUN REPORT

"Success came too early. When he was ten, he hit three homers in three times up in the Little League, and nothing has seemed worth while since."

"Your mother is a very remarkable woman, Herbert."

"Say 'Delighted to meet you.' I'll explain later."

"We don't sell them singly, Madam.
It breaks up the formation."

"I just wanted to see how I look from over here."

Rx
Closing out
ICE BAGS
and
ICE COLLARS
79¢
47¢

"They all look well on you, Madame."

"You should have seen this place Mother's Day. It was a madhouse."

NEXT WEEK- APRIL
RINGLING BROTHERS AND
BARNUM & BAILEY CIRCUS
MADISON SQUA
GARDEN

"My God, it's following us!"